★ the complete
Judge
Caligula

intro

★ The original Caligula was Emperor of Rome from AD 36-41. He was a megalomaniac, a tyrant, prone to heinous cruelty, and - though some historians dispute this - at least one leaf short of a laurel.

Because of his baldness and hairiness, he is said to have declared it a capital offence for anyone either to look down upon him as he passed in the street, or to mention goats in any context.

He once marched his troops to Gaul as a prelude to the invasion of Britain, but then made them collect seashells, which he called the spoils of the conquered ocean. Caligula had defeated Neptune by pinching his shell collection.

You're absolutely right, Mr Historian, no saner man has walked this earth.

If anything, writer John Wagner's Judge Caligula has even less leaves in his laurel. Parallels with his warped namesake abound, but taken still further. Where Emperor Caligula was supposed to have made his horse, Incitatus, a consul, Judge Caligula gives the post of Deputy Chief Judge to a goldfish. Judge Fish's word is henceforth law, and since the fish is unsurprisingly prone to shyness, Cal's interpretations of the odd "bloop" are deemed to mean anything from putting the dampers on Cal's idea of murdering the whole of Mega-City One to putting Judge Percy in a dress. As Cal notes, "An

excellent decision".

Where the Emperor was merely ruthless, the Judge paralyses his most faithful henchman and pickles him in vinegar. Where the Emperor was simply power-crazed, his Mega-City counterpart bans laughter. If TV sitcoms had been around at the time, his task would have been that much easier.

That Judge Cal is round the proverbial twist is not up for argument. He's so far round that he's turned a full 360° and is returning for another circuit.

This luxurious volume that you hold lovingly in your hands is the complete, unabridged and sorry tale of Judge Cal, from his early days in the Special Judicial Squad - a Gestapo-like outfit who investigate crimes committed by other judges - to his swansong as a crazed dictator in the flimsy guise of Chief Judge, sentencing the one hundred million-strong population of Mega-City One to death.

Defeating him was one of Judge Dredd's greatest tests, given that Cal had brainwashed almost every member of the Justice Department into his service. Aided only by Judge Giant and a motley band of ailing Tutors, Dredd has to take on not only the SJS and the overwhelming numbers of his once-colleagues, but a sadistic army of alien mercenaries employed by Cal, the Kleggs. It is only with the help of giant thicky and human

Batman team-up it's a shame, because it hasn't been published yet.

McMahon and Bolland are perhaps the two definitive Dredd artists; McMahon having worked on the strip since its birth, with Bolland joining in just under a year later. If you want to catch their work nowadays - and few bar your mother, surviving grandparents, and their loveable Machine. It's only a shame that Cal can't be there with them, making Death's killing quota look like household homicide. Unfortunately, he had a previous engagement with a paving slab.

Like all of history's crazed world-leader-pretends - Caesar, Hitler, Saddam - his notoriety will never fade. You hold in your hands the *Mein Kampf* of comics.

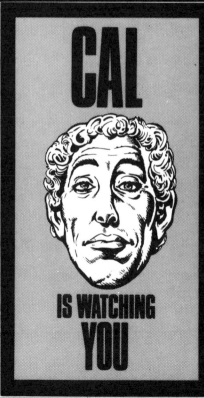

ISSUED BY THE MEGA-CITY ONE JUSTICE DEPARTMENT

bios

BRIAN BOLLAND is one of the UK's leading comic artists, having worked on many of the quintessential Judge Dredd *sagas during the early days of 2000AD. He then became one of the first British creators to work for DC in the States, on the* Camelot 3000 *maxi-series, and the celebrated* Killing Joke *graphic novel. He now concentrates on his* Mr Mamoulian *and* The Actress And The Bishop *strips, published in Europe, while drawing covers for* Animal Man, *the recent* Robin *mini-series and* The Greatest Joker Stories Ever Told *collection for DC. A collaboration with Grant Morrison has been mooted as his next major project.*

MIKE McMAHON is regarded by many as the definitive Judge Dredd *artist with his work on many of the early* Judge Dredd *strips for 2000AD, for whom he has also drawn* ABC Warriors, Ro-Busters, Slaine, The VCs *and various* Future Shocks. *His acclaimed* The Last American *mini-series was recently published by Epic in the US, and he now contributes* Muto Maniac *to Britain's new shock weekly,* Toxic.

JOHN WAGNER was largely responsible, with Pat Mills, for the renaissance of British comics in the 1970s, with the co-creation of Battle, Action *and* 2000AD. *Working under various pseudonyms and often with writer Alan-Grant, he has scripted countless* Judge Dredd *stories for 2000AD, as well as* Ace Trucking Co, Strontium Dog *and* Robo-Hunter. *While still working on* Dredd, *he has also written* The Outcasts *maxi-series for DC and* Nightbreed *and* The Last American *for Epic, and the* Bogie Man *mini-series for Fat-Man Press. He is currently working on* the Judge Dredd/Batman *team-up.*

THE COMPLETE JUDGE CALIGULA
1 85286 375 7

Published by Titan Books Ltd, 58 St Giles High St, London WC2H 8LH.

First published in two volumes June & December 1982.
This edition first published July 1991. *Judge Dredd* is © Fleetway Publications 1991.

10 9 8 7 6 5 4 3 2 1

Cover illustrations by Brian Bolland & Mike McMahon.

Printed in Singapore.

THE PHOTOGRAPHER DIED ALMOST AS HIS CAMERA FLASHED...

THAT'S THE *LAST* PICTURE YOU TAKE, CITIZEN!

AN HOUR LATER, AT DREDD'S APARTMENT...

YOU CAN'T GO IN THERE. JUDGE DWEDD'S ASLEEP—

WE'LL JUST HAVE TO WAKE HIM UP THEN!

WHAT THE...? MEN OF *JUDGE CAL'S SJS*—THE *SPECIAL JUDICIAL SQUAD*. THEY'RE ONLY MEANT TO INVESTIGATE CRIMES COMMITTED BY OTHER JUDGES.

YOU'D BETTER HAVE A GOOD EXPLANATION FOR THIS, QUINCY!

WE HAVE, DREDD—

YOU'RE UNDER ARREST— FOR *MURDER!*

THEN THANK DROKK YOU'RE NOT CHIEF JUDGE. LET'S GET ON WITH IT...

SOON, AT JUSTICE CENTRAL...

I JUST CAN'T BELIEVE THAT DREDD MURDERED THOSE NEWSMEN. NOT *DREDD.*

YOU'VE ALWAYS BEEN TOO SOFT ON THAT MURDERING DEVIL. IF *I* WAS CHIEF JUDGE I WOULDN'T EVEN GIVE HIM THE BENEFIT OF A TRIAL.

UNDER MEGA-CITY LAW, A SUSPECT JUDGE WAS TRIED BEFORE A COUNCIL OF FIVE. WITNESSES WERE BROUGHT FORWARD —

WALTER WAS OUTSIDE JUDGE DWEDD'S DOOR ALL DAY. JUDGE DWEDD NEVER LEFT HIS ROOM.

THAT ROBOT'S SICKENINGLY LOYAL. HE'S LYING. NEXT WITNESS!

THE EVIDENCE AGAINST DREDD WAS DAMNING...

IT WAS DREDD ALL RIGHT. I'D RECOGNISE HIS VOICE ANYWHERE.

A HERO, HE CALLED HIMSELF. I'D CALL HIM A STINKING MURDERER!

"BOX" PATON TOOK A PICTURE JUST AS THE EDITOR WAS SHOT. BEFORE THE SHUTTER CLOSED THE KILLER GOT OFF ANOTHER SHOT. ONLY JUDGE DREDD MOVES THAT FAST.

I...DON'T UNDERSTAND. I...HAVE NO MEMORY OF GOING TO THE MEGA-TIMES OFFICE...AND YET THERE'S NO REASON FOR THOSE MEN TO LIE.

GENTLEMEN, THE PENALTY FOR CRIMES BY A JUDGE IS TWENTY YEARS PENAL SERVITUDE ON THE COLONY OF TITAN. WE'VE HEARD THE EVIDENCE, NOW WE MUST DECIDE.

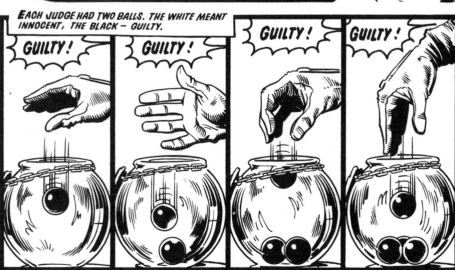

EACH JUDGE HAD TWO BALLS. THE WHITE MEANT INNOCENT, THE BLACK — GUILTY.

GUILTY!

GUILTY!

GUILTY!

GUILTY!

THE VERDICT MUST BE UNANIMOUS. VOTE, JUDGE GOODMAN.

VOTE — OR STAND DOWN AS CHIEF JUDGE AND LET ME TAKE YOUR PLACE.

LAUGH **THIS OFF, JACK-ASS!**

FREE! NOW I'VE GOTTA GET THIS SHUTTLE **TURNED! GOTTA** FIND THE MAN WHO **FRAMED** ME!

AT KENNEDY SPACEPORT, THERE WAS CONSTERNATION.

SIR, THE **0949** TO TITAN IS COMING BACK.... COULD BE TROUBLE.

GET A SECURITY DETAIL TO THE LANDING RUN. JUDGE DREDD'S ABOARD THAT SHUTTLE. HE'S DANGEROUS.

THE SHUTTLE GLIDED CLUMSILY DOWN. LANDINGS ARE NEVER EASY WITH A GUN AT YOUR HEAD--

SECURITY'S ALL READY FOR YOU, DREDD, YOU'LL BE A PRISONER AGAIN AS SOON AS THE SHUTTLE STOPS!

THEN **DON'T** STOP-- **KEEP MOVING!**

M-MY STARS! IT'S NOT SLOWING DOWN!

DIVE!

PENAL POD

SECURITY

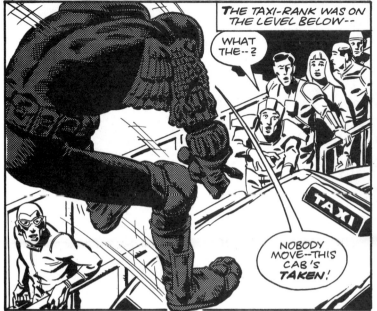

THE TAXI-RANK WAS ON THE LEVEL BELOW--

WHAT THE--?

NOBODY MOVE--THIS CAB'S TAKEN!

DRIVE! AND IF YOU EVER WANT TO WORK THIS RANK AGAIN, DON'T STOP TILL I TELL YOU!

Y-YES, S-S-SIR!

AT JUSTICE CENTRAL, DEPUTY CHIEF JUDGE CAL SUMMONED EVERY AVAILABLE JUDGE TO THE GRAND HALL--

I WANT DREDD AND I WANT HIM NOW! YOU'RE RELIEVED OF ALL OTHER DUTIES UNTIL HE'S FOUND!

A-ALL OF US, SIR? HAS THE CHIEF JUDGE OKAYED IT, SIR?

YES...YES... WHATEVER JUDGE CAL THINKS IS... BEST...

JUDGE CAL SNARLED...

DON'T EVER QUESTION MY AUTHORITY AGAIN, JUDGE OCHS! I'M HANDLING THINGS HERE UNTIL THE CHIEF JUDGE IS ... WELL AGAIN.

THE CHIEF JUDGE HAS GONE TO PIECES SINCE HIS VOTE CONDEMNED DREDD TO TITAN, JUDGE CAL WOULD JUST LOVE TO STEP INTO HIS SHOES--PERMANENTLY!

THERE FOLLOWED THE BIGGEST MAN-HUNT IN MEGA-CITY HISTORY...

WE'RE LOOKING FOR DREDD.

IN MY BAG?

ANYWHERE!

YOU WATS! YOU'LL NEVER FIND DWEDD!

CAN IT, RUST-BUCKET --OR WE'LL CAN YOU!

I'M WALTER TRY ME

JUDGE DREDD
JUDGE
THERE'S ONLY ROOM FOR ONE DREDD IN MEGA-CITY, AND THAT DREDD IS ME!
IT'S A FIGHT I CAN'T WIN! HOW CAN I KILL MYSELF?
DREDD
2000 A.D. Credit Card:
SCRIPT ROBOT JOHN HOWARD
ART ROBOT McCARTHY/EWINS
LETTERING ROBOT T. FRAME
COMPU-73E
BRING ME THE HEAD OF JUDGE DREDD!

JUDGE DREDD

IN **THE DAY THE LAW DIED!**

CHIEF JUDGE CLARENCE GOODMAN IS DEAD AND HIS KILLER, THE INSANE JUDGE CAL, HAS BECOME MEGA-CITY 1'S NEW CHIEF JUDGE. AMONG THE FIRST VICTIMS OF CAL'S REIGN OF FEAR IS JUDGE DREDD. SENTENCED TO **DEATH**, DREDD BREAKS **FREE** —

2000 A.D.
Credit Card:

SCRIPT ROBOT
JOHN HOWARD

ART ROBOT
MIKE McMAHON

LETTERING ROBOT
TOM KNIGHT

COMPU·73E

JUDGE PERCY SPEAKING, RED ALERT! *JUDGE DREDD HAS ESCAPED!*

JUDGE GIANT WAS HELPING DREDD...

MY INJURIES...SLOWING ME DOWN... LEAVE ME, GIANT...

NO WAY, BABY! MEGA-CITY *NEEDS* YOU!

EMERGENCY EXIT TUBES

THERE THEY ARE! HOLD IT!

GIANT LASHED OUT...

YOU'RE BLOCKIN' THE TUBES, DUDES!

AAAGH!

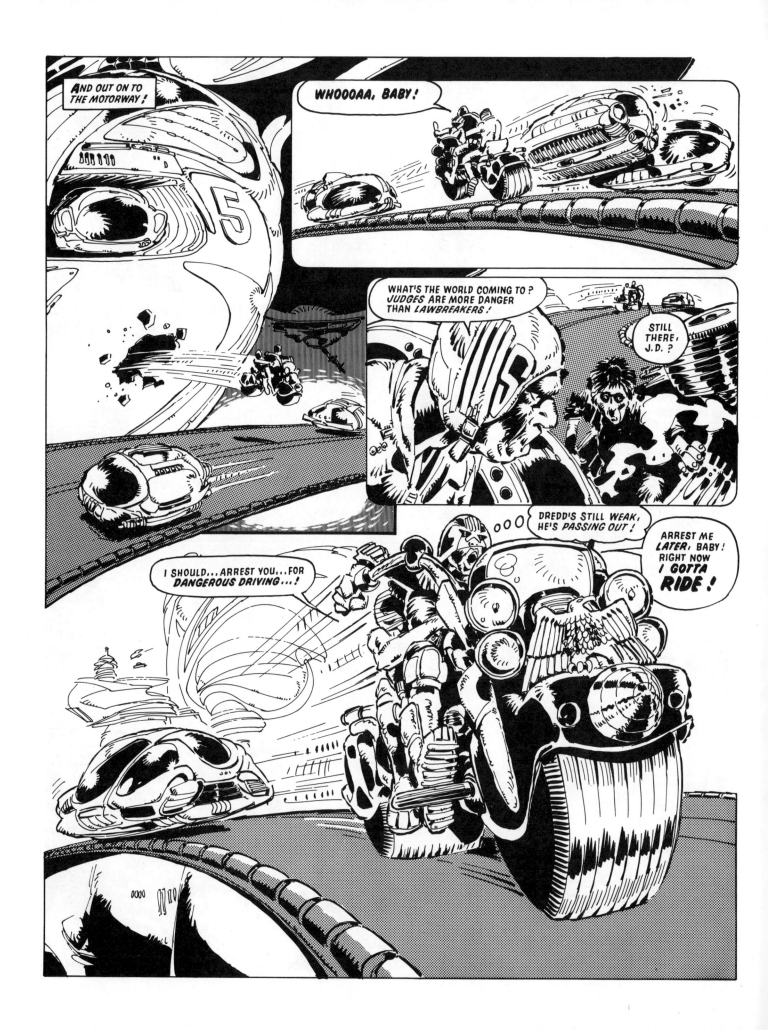

DEPUTY CHIEF JUDGE *FISH* SENTENCED THEM TO DRESS LIKE THAT, SIR. HE SAID IT WOULD BE A LESSON TO EVERY JUDGE TO BEHAVE LIKE *MEN* NOT *LITTLE GIRLS*.

HE DID? REALLY?

JUDGE CAL HAD APPOINTED A *GOLDFISH* AS HIS DEPUTY —

IT WOULDN'T DO TO OVERRULE JUDGE FISH'S DECISION. THE MEN MIGHT *LOSE CONFIDENCE* IN HIM!

AN EXCELLENT DECISION!

WELL, WHAT ARE YOU WAITING FOR? I WANT *EVERY MAN* ON THE STREETS LOOKING FOR DREDD—AND I *DON'T* WANT HIM *ALIVE!*

PHEW! IT WORKED!

NIGHT FELL AND JUDGE DREDD WAS STILL ON THE LOOSE. JUDGE SLOCUM SENT A MESSAGE OUT OVER EVERY TELEVISION CHANNEL—

THE HUGE REWARD BROUGHT MANY TAKERS—

HERE HE IS, JUDGE!

I-I'M ONLY P-PRETENDING!

"HAVE YOU SEEN THIS MAN

CHIEF JUDGE CAL OFFERS A REWARD OF *ONE MILLION CREDITS* FOR INFORMATION LEADING TO THE CAPTURE OF THE FUGITIVE *JUDGE DREDD.* CITIZENS ARE *ORDERED* TO BE ON THE LOOKOUT!

THAT'S DREDD, OFFICER. HE'S IN *DISGUISE*

RIK THE VIK

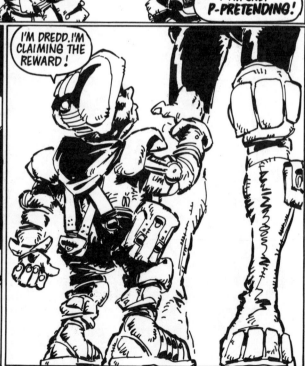

I'M DREDD. I'M CLAIMING THE REWARD!

NEXT PROG: *THE KLEGGS ARE COMING!*

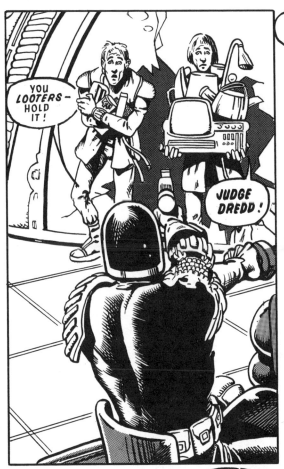

YOU LOOTERS— HOLD IT!

JUDGE DREDD!

A-AW, GEE, JUDGE, W-WE WAS ONLY TAKIN' A FEW THINGS. WE'RE ON YOUR SIDE.

NO LAWBREAKER IS ON MY SIDE. RETURN TO YOUR HOMES AND PLACE YOURSELVES UNDER HOUSE ARREST. I'LL DEAL WITH YOU LATER.

WE'RE FIGHTING FOR LAW AND ORDER— NOT AGAINST IT! ANYONE WHO FORGETS THAT WILL HAVE ME TO FACE. GOT THAT?

WE'RE WITH YOU ALL THE WAY, JUDGE DREDD.

BY AFTERNOON DREDD'S CITIZENS' ARMY HAD DRIVEN CAL'S MEN BACK TO THE STEPS OF THE HALL OF JUSTICE—

JUDGE CAL, YOU'RE UNDER ARREST!

YOU ARE SURROUNDED. THERE'S NO ESCAPE. SURRENDER QUIETLY AND MANY LIVES WILL BE SAVED.

JHQ

HOW BORING. THAT DREDD IS SUCH A STICKLER.

A STICKLER FOR WHAT, CHIEF JUDGE?

A STICKLER FOR EVERYTHING, YOU FOOL!

TELL HIM HE'LL HAVE MY ANSWER IN, OH... APPROXIMATELY FIVE MINUTES.

WANT **MEAT**!

ER, YES...

REMARKABLE RACE, THE KLEGGS. FIGHT FOR THE JOY OF KILLING AND TAKE PAYMENT ONLY IN **MEAT**. I THOUGHT I'D LET THEM EAT THE CITIZENS.

OH, NO, CHIEF JUDGE. THEY MIGHT GET A TASTE FOR HUMAN MEAT, AND THEN NONE OF US WOULD BE SAFE!

H'MM, GOOD POINT, SLOCUM. PITY. SEEMS A SHAME TO WASTE A CITY.

LATER, IN A SECRET PLACE IN THE CITY...

FOUR DEAD, THREE BADLY WOUNDED. JUDGE SCHMALTZ SAYS ONE OF THEM WON'T LAST THE NIGHT!

MEN WE COULDN'T AFFORD TO LOSE. WE'VE TAKEN A BAD SET-BACK TODAY!

TUTOR GRIFFIN

SUDDENLY THE VID-SCREEN LIT UP—

CITIZENS! TODAY'S REBELLION WAS UNFORGIVABLE. I AM CHIEF JUDGE NOW AND I WILL NOT BE DEFIED.

THEREFORE, TO TEACH YOU A LESSON, I HAVE DECIDED TO SENTENCE THE WHOLE CITY TO DEATH.

THE EXECUTIONS WILL BEGIN TOMORROW IN SECTOR 1, STARTING WITH *MR. AARON A. AARDVARK* AND FINISHING WITH *MR ZACHARY ZZIIZ*, THEN ON TO SECTOR 2 AND SO ON.

MEGA-CITY 1

ATOMIC WASTE-LAND

J

NOW, I WANT THINGS CARRIED OUT IN AN ORDERLY MANNER. REPORT TO YOUR EXECUTION STATIONS IN GOOD TIME. NO BARGING OR ROWDINESS IN THE QUEUES. AND BRING A BOOK IN CASE THERE IS A DELAY. THAT IS ALL.

THIS HAS BEEN A PUBLIC SERVICE ANNOUNCEMENT. FURTHER INFORMATION CAN BE OBTAINED FROM EXECUTION CONTROL [PHONE: 0378 223 908 2243 1267 20]

WHEEE-OOO! I KNEW THAT CAT WAS CRAZY, J.D., BUT I DIDN'T KNOW **HOW** CRAZY!

YES, GIANT! THE QUESTION IS, WHAT ARE WE GOING TO **DO** ABOUT IT!

NEXT PROG: **JUDGEMENT DAY**!

AND SO MEGA-CITY'S BLACKEST HOURS ROLLED ON...

A MAJESTIC SIGHT, JUDGE COX. THE WORLD HAS KNOWN MANY TYRANTS, BUT *I* AM THE GREATEST OF THEM ALL. A TRUE TYRANT. A *TYRANT'S TYRANT!*

MIND YOU, AT THIS RATE THE EXECUTIONS COULD TAKE *YEARS.* I'LL GET JUDGE SLOCUM TO SPEED THINGS UP WHEN HE ARRIVES!

AT THAT MOMENT, NEARBY—

LOOK OUT!

CRAZY DRIVERS!

GET IN, SLOCUM!

WHAT THE—

MOVE IT, BOY!

DREDD! I SUPPOSE YOU'RE GOING TO KILL ME!

...WRONG, SLOCUM. I'M GOING TO LET YOU LIVE— *BECAUSE* YOU'RE GOING TO GET CAL TO STOP THE EXECUTIONS!

Y-YOU'RE CRAZY! HOW CAN I MAKE CAL DO ANYTHING?

I'LL TELL YOU WHAT TO DO — *YOU JUST DO IT!*

JUDGE FISH DIED AT EXACTLY 9 A.M. — THE TIME OF THE FIRST EXECUTION. IT IS A *SIGN*.... IF THE *PEOPLE* DIE, SO DO THE *JUDGES*!

YES, YES...YOU'RE RIGHT. I SEE IT CLEARLY NOW!

CANCEL THE EXECUTIONS IMMEDIATELY. I AM GOING TO PREPARE JUDGE FISH'S FUNERAL.

THANK DROKK, HE FELL FOR IT! DREDD'S SMART. HE KNEW CAL WAS VERY *SUPERSTITIOUS*, AND HE PLAYED ON IT!

THE FUNERAL WAS ANNOUNCED OVER CITY-WIDE TELEVISION. JUDGE FISH'S ASHES WERE PLACED IN A GOLDEN BOWL, AND THAT AFTERNOON —

AFTER MY *DIVINE ACT OF MERCY* THE PEOPLE WILL TURN OUT IN THEIR MILLIONS TO *WORSHIP* ME.

MAKE UP

REST IN PEACE

REST IN PEACE

FISH

HIS WISDOM LIVES ON

GONE BUT NOT FORGOTTEN

JUSTICE CENTRAL

VERY WELL, WE WILL DENY THEM NO LONGER. LET THE FUNERAL BEGIN.

WITH A VANGUARD OF KLEGG MERCENARIES, THE PROCESSION MOVED SLOWLY OUT OF THE HALL OF JUSTICE —

JUDGE DREDD
THE DAY THE LAW DIED!

NOT EVEN JUDGE DREDD CAN HIDE FROM —

2000 A.D.
Credit Card:
SCRIPT ROBOT
J. HOWARD
ART ROBOT
M. McMAHON
LETTERING ROBOT
T. FRAME
COMPU·73E

AAAROOOooo!

AAAROOOooo!

THE HOUNDS OF KLEGG!

OKAY, GIANT—GO, GO, GO!

AMEN TO THAT, BABY!

CHIEF JUDGE—L-LOOK! TH-THEY'RE *GETTING AWAY!*

THEY WHAAAT? *THEY DARE!*

AS THE ROAD LINER SPED THROUGH THE CITY, A RED ALERT WENT OUT TO ALL JUSTICE DEPARTMENT UNITS! AND—

HOVER SHIP AHEAD!

I THINK I MADE THE TUNNEL BEFORE THEY SAW US!

I HOPE YOU'RE *RIGHT*, GIANT!

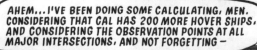

AHEM... I'VE BEEN DOING SOME CALCULATING, MEN. CONSIDERING THAT CAL HAS 200 MORE HOVER SHIPS, AND CONSIDERING THE OBSERVATION POINTS AT ALL MAJOR INTERSECTIONS, AND NOT FORGETTING—

YOU'RE NOT TEACHING CLASS NOW, KELSO! SKIP THE HOKUS-POKUS— JUST GIVE US *THE FACTS!*

MANY OF DREDD'S MEN WERE TUTORS FROM THE ACADEMY OF LAW—

HMMPH, THERE'S NO NEED TO BE SO RUDE, PEPPER. I WAS ONLY GOING TO SAY THAT OUR CHANCES OF SURVIVAL ARE A *MILLION TO ONE—AGAINST!*

THANKS, BABY... I NEEDED SOME CHEERING UP!

AAAAAGH!

CAL'S PERSONAL HOVER SHIP FLOATED DOWN —

THEY'VE CRASHED *RIGHT THROUGH* THE ROAD. *UGGN!* WHAT'S THAT *SICKENING STENCH?*

THAT'S THE OLD *OHIO RIVER* DOWN THERE — THEY USED TO CALL IT *THE BIG SMELLY!* IT GOT SO *POLLUTED* THEY HAD TO CONCRETE IT OVER!

THE BIG SMELLY! A FITTING END TO THAT *STINKER* DREDD!

GENTLEMEN, I FEEL *INSPIRED* TO MARK THIS OCCASION WITH A POEM. I CALL IT: *ODE SAID TO A DEAD DREDD...*

OH, DREDD! WOE, DREDD! NOWHERE LEFT TO GO, DREDD! ALL ALONE AND *SO* DEAD, IN THE BIG SMELLY.

ALL MOUTH AND NO HEAD, YOU PUT ON QUITE AN ACT, DREDD...UH, UH... NOW YOU'VE GOT B.O., DREDD, IN THE BIG SMELLY!

DO **YOU** LOVE ME, JUDGE COX? I MEAN, **REALLY** LOVE ME?

YES, JUDGE CAL. I.... I WOULD **DIE** FOR YOU!

WOULD YOU? THAT'S A **VERY** GENEROUS OFFER.

YOU'VE MADE ME FEEL A LOT BETTER, JUDGE COX. OFF YOU GO AND **DO IT**, THEN! I'LL LET YOU USE MY GUN.

B-B-B-BUT—

NO "BUTS", JUDGE COX! EITHER YOU LOVE ME OR YOU DON'T!

YES, SIR...

CAL KNOWS NO LIMITS! WE'VE GOT TO **KILL HIM**, SLOCUM — OR NEXT TIME IT WILL BE **US**!

WE WOULDN'T STAND A CHANCE WITH THOSE **KLEGGS** GUARDING HIM DAY AND NIGHT.

THERE WAS ONLY **ONE MAN** STRONG ENOUGH TO STAND AGAINST CAL! ONLY ONE MAN... **AND WE HELPED TO MURDER HIM!**

DREDD— SHOCK NEWS— NEXT PROG!

JUDGE DREDD

IN THE DAY THE LAW DIED!

IN MEGA-CITY ONE, CITY OF THE FUTURE, THE INSANE CHIEF JUDGE CAL WAS MAKING A BROADCAST TO THE PEOPLE...

CITIZENS, I HAVE NOT BEEN A BAD CHIEF JUDGE. TRUE, I DID EXECUTE SEVERAL MILLION OF YOU — BUT IT *COULD* HAVE BEEN *MORE!* AND AS FOR MY ALIEN MERCENARIES — WHY, THEY'RE NOT SO BAD ONCE YOU GET USED TO THEIR VICIOUS WAYS!

FROM THIS MOMENT ON, LAUGHTER IS *BANNED!* SMILING IS *BANNED!* CONVERSATION IS *BANNED!*

SOMETIMES AT NIGHT *VOICES* SPEAK TO ME, CITIZENS — VOICES OF ALL THE OLD CHIEF JUDGES WHO HAVE GONE TO THAT *GREAT SQUAD ROOM IN THE SKY...*

THEY SAY TO ME: "CAL, CAL, YOU'RE *TOO LENIENT WITH THEM! YOU MUST BE TOUGHER!"*

BUT ALWAYS MY HEART HAS CRIED "MERCY".

HAPPINESS IS ILLEGAL!

BUT ENOUGH IS ENOUGH! BY MOURNING THAT *TRAITOR DREDD* YOU HAVE INSULTED ME — *AND BY GRUD YOU'RE GOING TO SUFFER FOR IT!*

ALREADY, FIRES ARE BURNING IN EVERY STREET. BRING OUT YOUR *VALUABLES,* BRING OUT YOUR *DEAREST POSSESSIONS* — AND *DESTROY THEM!*

ANY CITIZEN FOUND HIDING ANY ITEM LIKELY TO CAUSE HAPPINESS —

WILL BE SHOT!

2000 A.D.
Credit Card:

SCRIPT ROBOT
J. HOWARD
ART ROBOT
M. McMAHON
LETTERING ROBOT
TOM FRAME

COMPU·73E

MIDGET, YOU HAVE BEEN CHOSEN TO PLAY THE PART OF *JUDGE DREDD* IN A *TV SPECTACULAR* I AM MAKING. IT WILL SHOW THE TRUE STORY OF MY *FEARLESS STRUGGLE* TO RESTORE LAW AND ORDER TO THIS CITY!

CONRED CONN, THE GREAT VID-PIC STAR!

THEY SAY HE'S THE HANDSOMEST MAN IN THE WORLD!

BUT HE RETIRED FROM SHOW BIZ. HE WANTED TO BE ALONE.

CITIZEN CONN, IT WILL BE YOUR PRIVILEGE TO PLAY THE GREATEST PART EVER WRITTEN— THE PART OF *ME!*

YOU KNOW I DON'T MAKE PICTURES ANY MORE, CHIEF JUDGE.

SUCH A PITY. SO HANDSOME, TOO. GRAMPUS, DON'T DAMAGE THIS HEAD WHEN YOU REMOVE IT.

IT WILL LEAVE HIS SHOULDERS CLEAN, JUDGE CAL.

D-DON'T KILL ME, CHIEF JUDGE! I-I'LL DO IT!

I KNEW YOU'D COME ROUND. SPEND A FEW MINUTES ON YOUR KNEES AND WE'LL FORGET THIS LITTLE TIFF EVER HAPPENED.

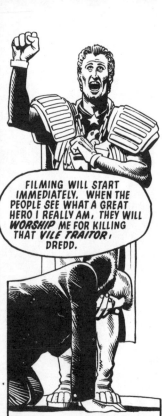

FILMING WILL START IMMEDIATELY. WHEN THE PEOPLE SEE WHAT A GREAT HERO I REALLY AM, THEY WILL *WORSHIP* ME FOR KILLING THAT *VILE TRAITOR*, DREDD.

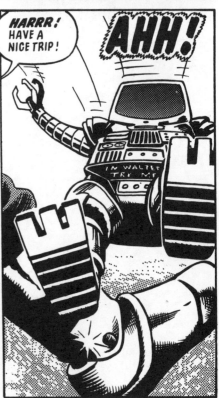

NEXT PROG: SPLAT!

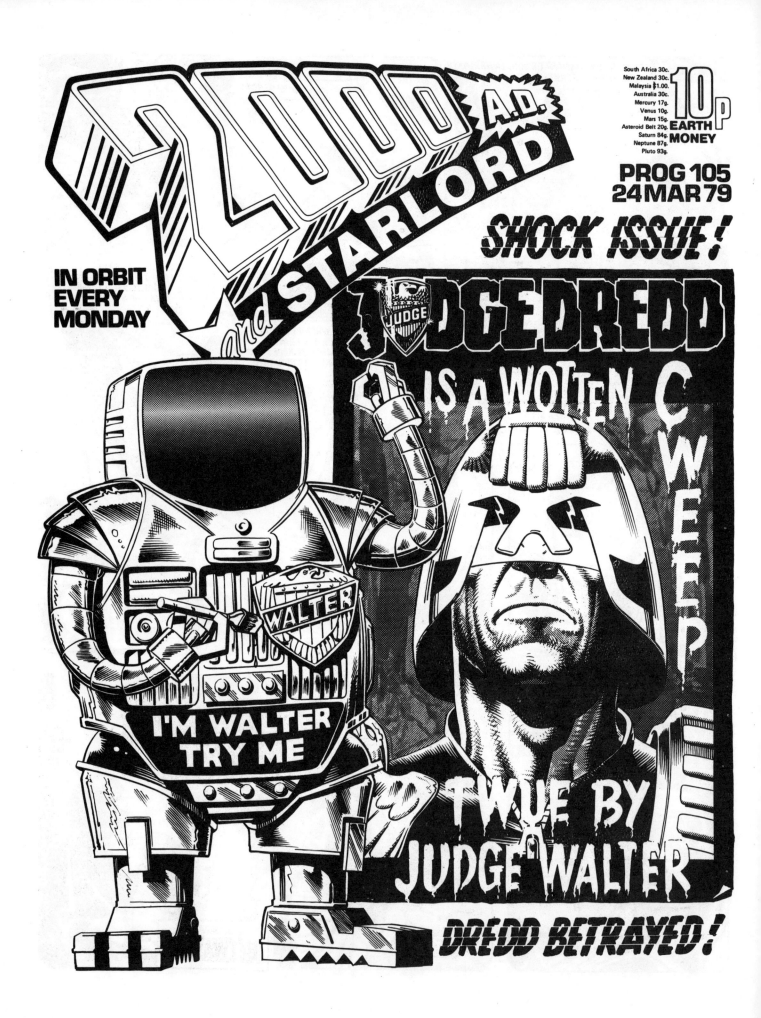

JUDGE DREDD

IN THE DAY THE LAW DIED!

IN ORDER TO GET A MAN INSIDE THE HALL OF JUSTICE, WHERE THE TYRANT JUDGE CAL RULES, JUDGE DREDD ENLISTS THE AID OF HIS ROBOSERVANT, WALTER. BUT WHEN WALTER IS TAKEN TO CAL, THINGS TURN NASTY —

IF I CAN'T KILL DREDD, AT LEAST I CAN KILL *YOU*! KNEEL, ROBOT!

YES, CHOP ME TO PIECES, GWEAT JUDGE CAL! WIP ME TO WOBO-SHWEDS! ONLY *PLEASE* DON'T SEND WALTER BACK TO THAT *CWEEP* JUDGE DREDD!

WHAT? DID YOU CALL DREDD... *A CREEP*?

B-BE BWAVE, WALTER. WEMEMBER WHAT JUDGE DWEDD TELL YOU TO SAY —

2000 A.D.
Credit Card:
SCRIPT ROBOT
J. HOWARD
ART ROBOT
EWINS/McCARTHY
LETTERING ROBOT
THOMAS
COMPU-73ε

YES, A WOTTEN, UNGWATEFUL WASCAL! JUDGE DWEDD COME HOME YELLING AND SHOOTING AND MAKING A DWEADFUL MESS AND WALTER WILL NEVER SCWUB OFF ALL THAT HOWWIBLE GWEEN KLEGG BLOOD —

HURRR!

SOWWY... ALL THAT P-PWETTY GWEEN KLEGG BLOOD...

AND DO JUDGE DWEDD SAY *"NICE TO SEE YOU, WALTER"* OR *"THANK YOU FOR KEEPING MY WOOM CLEAN, WALTER"*? NO! HE SAY: *"GET UP OFF YOUR KNEES, YOU SNIVELLING WOBOT!"*

WALTER TWY TO BE A *GOOD* WOBOT, AND JUDGE DWEDD TWEAT HIM LIKE *WUBBISH*! BUT WALTER HAVE PWIDE! PLEASE DON'T MAKE ME GO BACK TO HIM! *I HATE HIM!*

YES, FWANK, JUDGE DWEDD WAS *CWUEL.* HE USED TO BEAT WALTER WITH HIS *TWUNCHEON.*

YES, WOBIN. JUDGE DWEDD TOOK *BWIBES.* HE USED HIS BADGE TO MAKE HIMSELF WICH!

YES, WUSSEL, JUDGE DWEDD KILLED THE OLD CHIEF JUDGE! DWEDD WAS HUNGWY FOR *POWER.*

WITH FRIGHTENING SKILL, THE CITY'S LAST HERO WAS BEING TURNED INTO A *VILLAIN...*

EXTRA! EXTRA! MORE DIRT ON DREDD!

THAT DREDD! I'M BEGINNIN' TO BE GLAD HE *AIN'T* CHIEF JUDGE!

YEAH. AT LEAST YOU KNOW WHERE YOU ARE WITH CAL.

IT WAS DAYS BEFORE WALTER FOUND TIME FOR HIS REAL MISSION —

THAT'S IT FOR TONIGHT, JUDGE WALTER. TOMORROW YOU'RE BOOKED FOR *'THE LATE SHOW', 'THE LATE, LATE SHOW'* AND *'THE ELK'S BANQUET.'* SO GET SOME SLEEP.

WOBOTS DO NOT NEED *SLEEP,* JUDGE WICKS. GOOD NIGHT.

WALTER *HATE* TELLING ALL THESE *LIES,* BUT IT'S THE ONLY WAY TO HELP DEAR JUDGE DWEDD

UTHORIZED ERSONNEL ONLY

'CWIME BWIEFING WOOM'... THIS IS THE PLACE JUDGE DWEDD SAY!

DEATH DAY IN MEGA-CITY ONE! IN EVERY SECTOR NERVE GAS CONTAINERS WERE IN PLACE, WAITING FOR THE SIGNAL FROM THE INSANE JUDGE CAL THAT WOULD CONDEMN THE CITY TO MASS MURDER —

JUDGE DREDD

IN THE DAY THE LAW DIED!

BUT JUDGE DREDD HAD RALLIED THE MEGA-CITY JUDGES, AND NOW IN THE CITY STREETS LAW OFFICERS FIGHT FANATICALLY TO DRIVE OUT CAL'S ALIEN MERCENARIES —